Poems
Young G

Mia Sheen

Presentation by *BookLeaf Publishing*

Web: www.bookleafpub.com

E-mail: info@bookleafpub.com

ISBN: 9789357614191

First edition 2022

Dedicated to Mrs Tinsley, for being a wonderful English teacher and encouraging my love of poetry.

Candlelight

Through the darkness,
I saw a flame flickering.
The light of a soul burning brightly,
And the light was you.
You helped me through times of pain and
suffering.
The grief which came over me was calmed,
By your candlelight flicker.
When your light was extinguished,
The memory of you lit up inside me.
I became other people's candlelight,
The candlelight which you once were.

The Environment

All living things,
Whether they be big or small,
Plant or animal,
Need to be cared for.
The world as we know it,
Is slowly being destroyed.

We all need to help all creatures,
To save our planet,
So the next generations to come,
Can have a peaceful world,
That was intended upon this planet.

The environment is a cause of nature,
And we all need to help nurture it.

Shadow

Give me a sign,
That you're not just a shadow in the darkness,
A made-up figure in my mind.
The shadow of a person who used to calm my
restless mind,
But now stolen from life.
What came over the flesh and bones of the
shadow,
To leave me drowning in this sea of misery.
The once living replaced by a figment of my
imagination.
Hopes and dreams for you to come back one last
time,
But none to ever come true.

Sea

Tossing relentlessly,
This void of darkness.
Snatching lives from people.
Ending happiness with a single movement.
Many lives are lost at sea.

Forever Resting

I'm lost.
My conscience is wandering.
I'm dizzy.
I need to rest,
But if I rest now,
I might not get back up:
I may leave you.
Any second now,
There could be endless rest.
No way to ever get back to the people I love.
Lost in all of time,
The breath knocked out.
Never to walk and see this beautiful place again.
Never to laugh one last time.
My eyelids could flicker, then shut.
Forever.

Emotion haikus

Sadness
Broken heart, torn soul.
No hope, no love, no passion.
Mind and sense useless.

Anger
Bubbling hot rage.
Takes over your heart and mind.
This fire won't stop.

Happiness
Grows like a blossom.
Is made by people you love.
It's in all of us.

Devastation
The death of loved ones.
Causes the heart to cry out,
With deep suffering.

The Queen's Jubilee

The Queen speaks words of wisdom.
Guiding us, helping us.
Nurturing the Commonwealth and its people.

We plant trees to celebrate the Platinum Jubilee
of our beloved lady of the Nation,
The Queen,
Queen Elizabeth II.

Tree Haiku for The Platinum Jubilee

As time passes by,
Trees start to grow, colour spreads,
Auburn, emerald.

In the winter months,
The trees are bare and leafless,
Or covered in snow.

Seasons Haikus

Spring
Flowers are growing.
The winter is whisked away.
Life is beginning.

Summer
The sun is shining.
The pools are full of water.
Ice cream is eaten.

Autumn
Leaves fall off of trees.
Hibernation has begun.
Winter is coming.

Winter
Winter is here now.
Animals sleep peacefully.
We are shivering.

Free

Gliding out,
Shadows,
Black walls,
Heart pounding,
Running,
Thinking,
"Need to rest",
Breath bursting,
Falling to the ground,
Eyes closing,
Free at last.

Moths

The speckled, freckled moths,
Were dancing to and fro,
But when the predators start to appear,
They all hide away in fear,
Camouflaging in with branches,
Instead of fluttering little dances,
They rest in peace.

In the morn' they wake and flutter,
Flying round like the trickle of butter,
Passing their characteristics on,
They lay their eggs on and on,
Children, grandchildren, year after year,
Lots of them hatch and appear and appear.

The Bully and The Bullied

Dream-snatcher
Hope-drowner
Happiness-tearer
Day-domineerer
Hard-hearted

Giver-upper
Mercy-shower
Punch-absorber
Tear-crier
Unhappiness-displayer

Acrostic Animals

Dirty paws
Oh so cute
Great companion

Cute
Adorable
The best

Radish eater
Awesome
Bunny
Big hopper
Incredible
Terrific

Beautiful
Insect eater
Really colourful
Dainty

Honey coloured
Absolutely fluffy
Mammal
So cute
Tubby

Easy to love
Rodent

Slithery
Never put your fingers in their mouths!
Anacondas and adders
Killers
Eat mammals

Green
Edible to birds
Cold-blooded
Killer of insects
One inch

Magnificent
Orangutan
Nit pickers
King Kong
Eat bananas
Yummy yellow snacks

Large
Incredible
One of the big cats
Not a herbivore

Terrific
Incredibly big cat

Gigantic
Eat meat
Roar

Lovely
Leaf eater
Are fluffy
Malts its fur
Amazing

High
Obstacle jumper
Rideable
Sleek
Elegant

The Queen's Passing - Prince Philip's Voice

As the breath left her resting body,
Tears were shed and goodbyes were said.
I stood silently by her bed, whispering softly,
"Come my Lilibet, your work here is done."
Her spirit rose and wrapped me in a warm embrace,
"I'm coming home!"
We walked hand in hand past all the sorrowful faces,
And way up into the heavens.

Refugees

As we fled from our war-torn country,
More and more people were captured
And were taken into prison camps.
We're just looking for a place to call home.

War had broken put.
Bombs were being dropped.
People were being taken.
Men were forced to join the army.

My papa had to join the army,
I haven't seen him in months.
My mama keeps on crying,
She can barely sleep at night.

We've been turned away many times,
What have we done to deserve that?
Why is the world so cruel?
We're just looking for a place to call home.

Celebrations Haikus

Easter
Chocolate eggs and treats.
Animals are being born.
The resurrection.

Birthdays
Presents are given.
Excited squeals from children.
It's a day for you.

Halloween
Lots and lots of sweets.
The shouts of trick or treating.
Dress up scarily.

Christmas
Glistening snow falls.
Lots of love and reunions.
Christmas trees stand proud.

My Summer Swim

Swimming peacefully,
The calm waves splashing over me.
I love the ocean for many reasons.
Maybe because of the deep blue colour,
Or maybe because of the sun
Making the water glow.

I could hear the shrill cry of a dolphin,
Vibrating,
Vibrating,
Vibrating,
Through the ocean

Then I saw her,
The most beautiful dolphin I had ever seen.
But then it struck me:
She was swimming away from something,
But what...?

The End of My Summer Swim

Multiple rows of razor-sharp teeth
Emerged from the water.
Fear took over me
And I started to panic.

I screamed for help but
I soon realised no-one could hear me.

Suddenly, a smooth body
Lifted me out of the water
And swam me back to shore.
I realised that it was
The dolphin from this morning.
The dolphin had just saved my life!

Natural haikus

Midnight Sky
Stars are twinkling in
The pitch black, midnight, dark sky
Like diamonds on card.

The Sun
The blazing hot sun
Reached down towards me with its
Fiery fingers.

The Stream
The gurgling stream
Raced down the ginormous hill
As a heron waits.

Rainbow
Rain and sun has made
A myriad of colours
In the bright blue sky.

My Biggest Fear

My biggest fear is being alone;
I'm scared of all the people I love
And care about leaving me.
Sometimes I do things I regret,
And so do they,
Although they'll never stop loving me.

But what if they all leave me?
Surrounded by walls of sadness and grief.
So, I will take advantage of the time
I have with these people,
Who I hold so dearly in my heart.

The End of School

I woke up with a smile on my face.
It's the last day of school, I thought.

The day felt so long,
But everywhere I went,
There were grins on people's faces.
It was 14:59 now,
3...2...1...
The bell went.
Everyone went out into the warm sunshine.

Although my journey at Primary had just ended,
There was a new chapter to begin.

The Loss of a Loved One

The day I lost one of the things I loved the most,
My whole life changed forever.
Endless tears would stream down my face,
As I thought of the precious
Time we'd spent together.
The grief and sorrow which came over me
Caused my heart to cry out.

In my heart, a massive hole had been left,
Because the one thing I held
So dearly in my heart,
Had been taken away from me.

I have things that were hers,
That I wish she was still here to see:
One of her old toys,
A collar I made for her,
A letter I wrote smudged with tears,
And a card from the place that put her down.

I miss her every single day,
And I just wish she could come back
One last time,
So I could see her again.

The pain that her death has
Caused is nearly unbearable,
But, eventually, I will see her again.